IRON MAN

IRON MAN

"HEART OF STEEL"
WRITER: Fred Van Lente
PENCILER: James Cordeiro
INKER: Scott Koblish
COLORIST: Studio F's Martegod Gracia
LETTERER: Blambot's Nate Piekos
COVER ARTIST: Michael Golden
ASSISTANT EDITOR: Nathan Cosby
EDITOR: Mark Paniccia

"THE TITANIUM TRAP"
WRITER: Fred Van Lente
PENCILER: James Cordeiro
INKER: Scott Koblish
COLORIST: Studio F's Martegod Gracia
LETTERER: Blambot's Nate Piekos
COVER ARTISTS: David Nakayama, Gary Martin
& Christina Strain
EDITOR: Nathan Cosby
CONSULTING EDITOR: Mark Paniccia

"SEVEN RINGS HATH THE MANDARIN"
WRITERS: Jeff Parker & Paul Tobin
PENCILER: Alvin Lee
INKER: Terry Pallot
COLORIST: Wilfredo Quintana
LETTERER: Blambot's Nate Piekos
COVER ARTISTS: David Nakayama & Christina Strain
EDITORS: Nathan Cosby & Mark Paniccia

"THERE'S AN APE FOR THAT!"
WRITER: Paul Tobin
ARTIST: Craig Rousseau
COLOR ARTIST: Veronica Gandini
LETTERER: Dave Sharpe
COVER ARTISTS: Ed McGuinness & Chris Sotomayor
ASSISTANT EDITOR: Michael Horwitz
EDITOR: Nathan Cosby

"EMPLOYEE OF THE MONTH"
STORY: Fred Van Lente
SCRIPT: Margot Blankier
ARTIST: Juan Santacruz
COLOR ARTIST: Chris Sotomayor
LETTERER: Dave Sharpe
EDITOR: Nathan Cosby
CONSULTING EDITOR: Mark Paniccia

Collection Editor: Cory Levine
Assistant Editors: Alex Starbuck & Nelson Ribeiro
Editors, Special Projects: Jennifer Grünwald & Mark D. Beazley
Senior Editor, Special Projects: Jeff Youngquist
Senior Vice President of Sales: David Gabriel
SVP of Brand Planning & Communications: Michael Pasciullo

Editor In Chief: Axel Alonso
Chief Creative Officer: Joe Quesada
Publisher: Dan Buckley
Executive Producer: Alan Fine

MARVEL UNIVERSE IRON MAN. Contains material originally published in magazine form as MARVEL ADVENTURES IRON MAN #1, FREE COMIC BOOK DAY 2007 (MARVEL ADVENTURES), FREE COMIC BOOK DAY 2008 (MARVEL ADVENTURES), FREE COMIC BOOK DAY 2010 (IRON MAN: SUPERNOVA) and IRON MAN: GOLDEN AVENGER #1. First printing 2013. ISBN# 978-0-7851-8426-3. Published by MARVEL WORLDWIDE, INC., a subsidiary of MARVEL ENTERTAINMENT, LLC. OFFICE OF PUBLICATION: 135 West 50th Street, New York, NY 10020. Copyright © 2007, 2008, 2010 and 2013 Marvel Characters, Inc. All rights reserved. All characters featured in this issue and the distinctive names and likenesses thereof, and all related indicia are trademarks of Marvel Characters, Inc. No similarity between any of the names, characters, persons, and/or institutions in this magazine with those of any living or dead person or institution is intended, and any such similarity which may exist is purely coincidental. **Printed in the U.S.A.** ALAN FINE, EVP - Office of the President, Marvel Worldwide, Inc. and EVP & CMO Marvel Characters B.V.; DAN BUCKLEY, Publisher & President - Print, Animation & Digital Divisions; JOE QUESADA, Chief Creative Officer; TOM BREVOORT, SVP of Publishing; DAVID BOGART, SVP of Operations & Procurement, Publishing; RUWAN JAYATILLEKE, SVP & Associate Publisher, Publishing; C.B. CEBULSKI, SVP of Creator & Content Development; DAVID GABRIEL, SVP of Publishing Sales & Circulation; MICHAEL PASCIULLO, SVP of Brand Planning & Communications; JIM O'KEEFE, VP of Operations & Logistics; DAN CARR, Executive Director of Publishing Technology; SUSAN CRESPI, Editorial Operations Manager; ALEX MORALES, Publishing Operations Manager; STAN LEE, Chairman Emeritus. For information regarding advertising in Marvel Comics or on Marvel.com, please contact Niza Disla, Director of Marvel Partnerships, at ndisla@marvel.com. For Marvel subscription inquiries, please call 800-217-9158. **Manufactured between 11/12/2012 and 1/7/2013 by SHERIDAN BOOKS, INC., CHELSEA, MI, USA.**

10 9 8 7 6 5 4 3 2 1

SEMI-RIGID CHESTPLATE: ENGAGED

INTERNAL CARDIOVERTER: 93%...97%... ON-LINE

shhhh-THUNK

GAUNTLETS: ENGAGED

CLIKK

MAGNETOMOTIVE REPULSOR RAY PROJECTORS: 93%...97%...ON-LINE

ssss-SNAP

3-D KNITTED "SKIN®" FLEXI-IRON™ SHEATHS: ENGAGED

SUB-DERMAL CONTROL INTERFACE: 93%... 97%... ON-LINE

sssh-SNAP   *sssh-SNAP*

SECONDARY WEAPONS SYSTEMS:
• **UNI-BEAM® 93%...97%...ON-LINE**
• **ENERGY SABRE: 93%...97%...ON-LINE**
• **POLYBOND CAPTURE FOAM: 93%...97%...ON-LINE**

HELMET: ENGAGED

sssh-THUNK

OPTICAL SYSTEMS:
• **TARGETING VIEW: 93%...97%...ON-LINE**
• **FULL E.M. SPECTRUM VIEW: 93%...97%...ON-LINE**
• **MAGNETIC RESONANCE IMAGER: 93%...97%...ON-LINE**

Vrr-RRRRNNNN

HIGH-SPEED, DUO-SOURCE, GYRO-STABILIZED BOOT TURBINES: 93%...97%...

...ON-LINE

THE NEWS FLASH SAID ADVANCED IDEA MECHANICS HAS TARGETED THE **FEDERAL RESERVE BANK** OF NEW YORK.

THAT'S AT THIRTY-THREE LIBERTY STREET IN MANHATTAN. I'LL UPLOAD THE COORDINATES INTO YOUR G.P.S. NOW--

DON'T BOTHER, RHODEY...

HEART OF STEEL

Written by FRED VAN LENTE   Penciled by JAMES CORDEIRO   Inked by SCOTT KOBLISH
Colored by STUDIO F's MARTEGOD GRACIA   Lettered by BLAMBOT's NATE PIEKOS
Cover by MICHAEL GOLDEN   Assistant Editor – NATHAN COSBY   Editor – MARK PANICCIA
Editor in Chief – JOE QUESADA   Publisher – DAN BUCKLEY

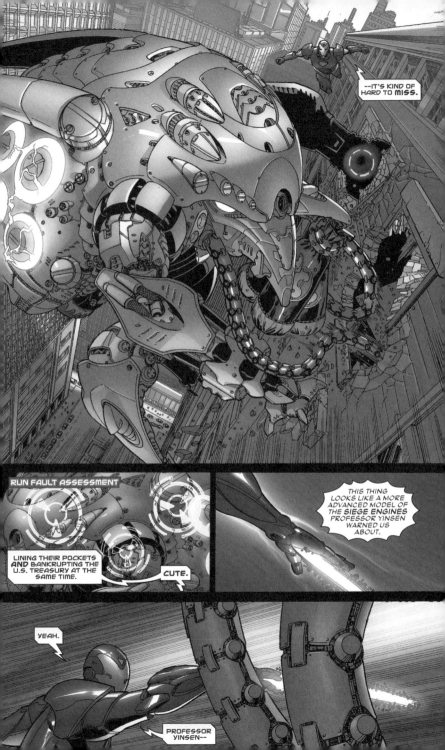

THEY'VE CERTAINLY PROVIDED US WITH EVERYTHING WE'D NEED TO FORGE AN *ARSENAL* UNLIKE ANYTHING THE WORLD HAS EVER *SEEN.*

WHAT MAKES THEM THINK WE WON'T JUST TURN THE WEAPONS WE MAKE ON *THEM* AND BUST OUR WAY *OUT* OF HERE?

FOR ONE THING, THEY ARE *WATCHING* US QUITE CLOSELY.

I AM QUITE SURE THIS ROOM IS *BUGGED* AS WELL.

AND THEY OUTNUMBER US A THOUSAND TO *TWO.* EVEN IF WE WERE ABLE TO ARM OURSELVES, WITHOUT ANY KIND OF PROTECTION WE'D BE CUT DOWN *INSTANTLY--*

YES...THAT ALL MAKES SENSE-- ≳*Unnnnh*≲

AND THIS...HEART CONDITION...IS NO *JOKE.*

AND LOOK AT THIS. THEY'VE EVEN DUMPED THE WRECKAGE OF THE OSPREY-1 IN HERE TO MOCK ME...FLAUNT THEIR POWER.

I SUPPOSE... A.I.M. IS *RIGHT.* WE HAVE NO OTHER *CHOICE.*

LET'S GET TO *WORK.*

<....ALL **BRAZIL** HOLDS ITS **BREATH** IN ANTICIPATION OF THE ARRIVAL OF BILLIONAIRE INVENTOR **TONY STARK** IN HIS NEW SUB-ORBITAL **SPACEPLANE!>***

<THIS EXPERIMENTAL JET SHOOTS **STRAIGHT** UP INTO OUTER SPACE AT A **KILOMETER A SECOND** BEFORE DROPPING BACK DOWN TO ITS INTENDED DESTINATION, LITERALLY **HOPPING** BETWEEN CONTINENTS!>

<HER **INAUGURAL** FLIGHT FROM NEW YORK TO RIO DE JANEIRO-- AN **ELEVEN-HOUR** TRIP IN REGULAR AIRCRAFT--IS TAKING LESS THAN **FORTY-FIVE** MINUTES TODAY!>

*TRANSLATED FROM PORTUGUESE.

<**THERE! I** CAN SEE A **SPECK**... GROWING IN THE SKY--IT MUST BE THE SPACEPLANE **DESCENDING**--ALONG WITH... ANOTHER **SPECK**....COULD THAT BE-- >

<**IT IS!** GUARDING THE JET'S APPROACH IS STARK INTERNATIONAL'S FAMED **HEAD OF SECURITY**-->

<--THE **INVINCIBLE IRON MAN!**>

THE titanium trap

FRED VAN LENTE WRITER   **JAMES CORDEIRO** PENCILER   **SCOTT KOBLISH** INKER   **STUDIO F'S MARTEGOD GRACIA** COLORIST   **BLAMBOT'S NATE PIEKOS** LETTERER

NAKAYAMA, MARTIN & STRAIN COVER ARTISTS   **MARK PANICCIA** CONSULTING EDITOR   **NATHAN COSBY** EDITOR   **JOE QUESADA** EDITOR IN CHIEF   **DAN BUCKLEY** PUBLISHER

NO...ACTUALLY, I THINK YOU'RE DONE NOW...
...DR. ALVES.
BUT--I WAS TOLD--YOU'D BE PATROLLING THE PERIMETER TONIGHT--
OH--THAT.
THAT WAS A LIE.
STARK DEDUCED THAT THE SECURITY CAMERAS DIDN'T PICK UP THE THIEF LEAVING THE PLANT...
BECAUSE HE NEVER ACTUALLY LEFT.
BUDGET CUTS HALTED CONSTRUCTION IN THIS SECTOR WEEKS AGO.
WHERE ELSE COULD SOMEBODY SET UP HIS OWN PRIVATE LAB WITHIN THE STARK BRAZIL FACILITY?
OUR BELOVED BOSS DIDN'T GIVE ME MUCH OF A CHOICE, IRON MAN.
HE CANCELLED MY GENETICALLY-MODIFIED METAL-AFFINITY-BACTERIA PROJECT--WHICH INCREASES THE STRENGTH OF HIS FLEXI-IRON A HUNDRED-FOLD...
...TURNING IT INTO FLEXI-TITANIUM!
ALLOW ME TO DEMONSTRATE!
SKRUNCH

END

WHO DESIGNED THIS DELIGHTFUL DISPLAY OF DARING DISTINCTION? NONE OTHER THAN
AMOROUS AUTHORS—JEFF PARKER & PAUL TOBIN! PENCIL PURVEYOR—ALVIN LEE!
INK EMBELLISHER—TERRY PALLOT! COLOR CREATOR—WILFREDO QUINTANA!
WORD WRANGLER—NATE PIEKOS! COVER CRAFTERS—NAKAYAMA & STRAIN!
PLEASANT PRODUCER—RICH GINTER! ELEGANT EDITORS—NATHAN COSBY & MARK PANICCIA!
JOE QUESADA—THE CHIEF OF ALL EDITORS! AND PIOUS PUBLISHER—DAN BUCKLEY!

MANDARIN'S RINGS!

SHAPE REARRANGER BEAM

GRAVITY BEAM

IMPACT BEAM

FIRE BLAST

VORTEX BEAM

ELECTRIC BLAST

DISINTEGRATION BEAM

MIND CONTROL

BLACK LIGHT BEAM

ICE BLAST

OUR HEROES!

IRON MAN

BRILLIANT-ARMORED INVENTOR

HULK

GAMMA-POWERED STRONGMAN

SPIDER-MAN

SPIDER-POWERED WEB-SLINGER

SPECIAL GUEST STAR

ANT-MAN

SHRINKING ANT COMMUNICATOR

GOOD MORNING, MR. STARK. WOULD YOU PREFER MOZART OR CHOPIN THIS MORNING?

ACTUALLY, LET'S GO WITH SIBELIUS'S VALSE TRISTE.

VERY GOOD, SIR.

OINK!

OINK!

OINK!

SQUEEEEAL!

OINK!

HUZZAT? IM'A GET UP? WHUFFO LARM CLOCK?

WE NOW RETURN TO, "FRANKENSTEIN VS. FIN FANG FOOM!"

THIS IS A PRIORITY ONE EMERGENCY CALL.

EEEEN EEEN EEEEN EEEN

THIS IS A PRIORITY ONE EMERGENCY CALL.

EEEEN EEEN EEEEN EEEN

MINUTES LATER...

WHICH WAY TO THE APES?

IRON MAN. I'M KATE McMILLAN, THE DIRECTOR HERE.

HOWDY. I'M NOVA.

WHAT'S ALL THIS ABOUT?

TWO HOURS AGO, THE RED GHOST ESCAPED FROM HIS STASIS CELL.

HE'S CERTAIN TO COME HERE TO THIS CONFINEMENT ZOO FOR STRANGELY POWERED ANIMALS.

BECAUSE WE'RE HOLDING HIS SUPER-APES HERE?

EXACTLY. EVEN ON HIS OWN, THE RED GHOST'S ABILITY TO TURN INTANGIBLE MAKES HIM A FORMIDABLE OPPONENT.

BUT WHEN HE'S TEAMED WITH HIS SUPER-APES AND THEIR UNCANNY ABILITIES, HE'S VIRTUALLY UNSTOPPABLE.

I KNOW THAT REED RICHARDS DESIGNED YOUR DEFENSES, BUT EVEN HE COULDN'T FORESEE HAVING TO KEEP OUT AN INTANGIBLE MAN.

WHICH IS WHY I BROUGHT THIS PORTABLE STASIS FIELD GENERATOR. IT SHOULD TRAP EVEN THE RED GHOST.

FOLLOW ME, PLEASE.

CANDY? I DON'T HAVE **THAT** LISTED IN MY INTERNAL FILES.

YOU CAN'T LEARN **EVERYTHING** FROM A COMPUTER. **SOMETIMES** YOU HAVE TO COME OUT OF YOUR **SHELL.**

ZZZZING!

OOO. I **REALLY** DIDN'T MEAN THAT TO BE RUDE...IT'S JUST THAT I'VE GOTTEN TO **KNOW** IGOR AND THE OTHERS. THEY'RE **EXTREMELY** INTELLIGENT.

HOW INTELLIGENT? LIKE... **DOG** LEVEL, OR **REALITY SHOW CONTESTANT,** OR EVEN **HUMAN**-LEVEL INTELLIGENCE?

LOW-LEVEL HUMAN, I'D SAY.

WE'VE BEEN DOING A LOT OF TESTS WITH THEM. **SOME** WITH MIKHLO AND PEOTR, BUT **MOSTLY** WITH IGOR. HE'S PROVEN THE MOST RECEPTIVE TO THIS NEW ENVIRONMENT.

WHILE **MIKHLO** AND **PEOTR** REMAIN PROBLEMATICALLY DEDICATED TO THEIR **OLD** LIFE... **IGOR** CONSISTENTLY CHOOSES **CANDY** OVER THE RED GHOST IN ASSOCIATION TESTS.

OF COURSE, **WE HERE** LIKE TO THINK IGOR LIKES **US** MORE THAN THE **CANDY.**

THESE **ARE** PRETTY GOOD.

ARE ALL DEFENSES WORKING AT FULL CAPACITY?

YES, WE RUN *DAILY* CHECKS, AND WHEN YOU SENT OUT THE GENERAL *ALARM* WE--

OHH. *WHAT'S THAT?*

IS IT SOMETHING OF *YOURS?* SOME DEFENSIVE *DRONE* THAT--?

IT'S *NOT* OURS!

TO ME, MY SUPER-APES! MIKHLO! IGOR! PEOTR! NOW THAT I HAVE *BROKEN FREE* OF MY CURSED CONFINEMENT, WE SHALL FORM OUR TEAM ONCE AGAIN!

BREAK FREE! BREAK FREE AND MEET ME AT LOCATION M-22, AND WE SHALL--

ZZZZNT

SKROOOWWNT

THIS IS *BAD.* ALL OUR PRECAUTIONS WERE FOR KEEPING THE RED GHOST *OUT.* I HADN'T THOUGHT ABOUT HIM ORDERING THE *APES* TO *FREE* THEM-SELVES.

BUT...THIS IS BASICALLY A *PRISON ZOO, RIGHT?* I MEAN...THE APES *CAN'T ESCAPE?*

HUH?

WHAT?

CRINKLE CRINKLE

EE-CHEEEE!

AWWW, DUDE!

LAME!

WHAT'S GOING ON?

THAT APE WAS ON MY HEAD!

I THINK IGOR HAS SWITCHED SIDES. LIKE I WAS SAYING EARLIER...HE REALLY DOESN'T LIKE THE RED GHOST ANYMORE.

I THINK HE WANTS TO BE FRIENDS WITH THE TWO OF YOU.

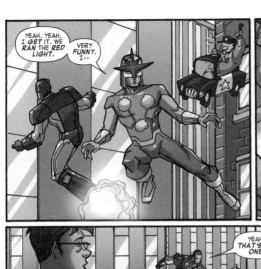

YEAH. YEAH. I *GET* IT. WE *RAN* THE *RED* LIGHT. I--

VERY *FUNNY.*

AHH, *COME ON,* IGOR!

WE *HAVE* TO *STOP* THE *RED GHOST!* THE *RED GHOST...* REMEMBER?

YEAH. *THAT'S* THE *ONE.*

LET'S GET HIM *BACK* INTO *PRISON,* AND *THEN* HAVE A LOT OF *CANDY.* OKAY?

YEAH! NOW WE'RE *TALKING!*

THAT IS ONE *BIG BABOON.*

DOWN TH--*HEY!*

I'LL START PREPPING THE *STASIS FIELD GENERATOR,* AND LET'S GO IN *QUIET* AND TRY TO TAKE THEM BY--

IGOR STOPPED THE BRICKS, BUT WE'RE BEING OVERWHELMED *AGAIN!*

I *THINK* I'VE GOT AN *IDEA!* MIKHLO'S *STRONG,* BUT HE STILL NEEDS A PLACE TO STAND IN ORDER TO REALLY *USE* HIS STRENGTH!

SRRAAAKOOOW

GRAAARRRR!

AND HE NEEDS TO *BREATHE!*

OOOK!

SEE? *THIS* IS WHY YOU SHOULD *ALWAYS* SHAVE YOUR BACK!

GRARRRR!

OKAY, KONG. *MY* UNIFORM HAS INTERNAL *SUPPORT* SYSTEMS!

BUHH-LOOOOGE

BUT LET'S JUST SEE HOW LONG *YOU* CAN HOLD YOUR BREATH!

JUST YOU AND ME, IGOR.

IGOR! YOU'RE SUPPOSED TO FIGHT ON MY SIDE!

NOT ANYMORE, GHOST! HE'S WITH THE GOOD GUYS, NOW!

WELL, AT LEAST UNTIL THE CANDY RUNS OUT.

SO BE IT!

ZEEEEENNN

IGOR...LEAVE HIM ALONE! AS SOON AS MY STASIS GENERATOR IS CHARGED THE RED GHOST WILL BE AN EASY CATCH!

IT'S PEOTR THAT'S THE DANGER RIGHT NOW.

EEEGHH! EEEKK!

SOGGY APE DELIVERY SERVICE!

WHO ORDERED THE GORILLA?

OOK

HOW'S IT GOING WITH THE ORANGUTAN?

HIS POWERS ARE TOO STRONG. CAN'T EVEN GET CLOSE UNLESS WE CAN FIND A WAY TO NEUTRALIZE HIS--

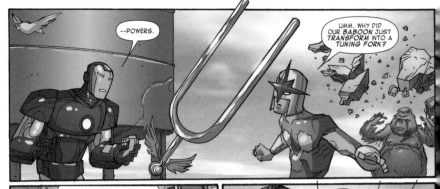

--POWERS.

UMM. WHY DID OUR BABOON JUST TRANSFORM INTO A TUNING FORK?

PEOTR'S POWERS MUST WORK ON A CERTAIN WAVELENGTH! IGOR'S EMITTING A FREQUENCY THAT'S MOMENTARILY CANCELING THE ORANGUTAN'S ABILITIES!

HE'S VULNERABLE NOW!

GOT HIM!

THWOKK

THAT LEAVES ONLY THE RED GHOST, AND NOW THAT MY STASIS FIELD GENERATOR IS WARMED UP, WE CAN--

SPRKNT

FEEENNT

HAH!

SO MUCH FOR THAT, IRON MAN. AND NOW THAT YOU CAN'T STOP ME, I'LL BE BACK FOR MY APES ANOTHER TIME.

IN FACT, SINCE I'M COMPLETELY INTANGIBLE, MAYBE I'LL JUST WAIT UNTIL THEY WAKE UP, AND--

...THE END.

Speak of the devil. Just the gal we wanted to see.
Why isn't the electroshock code working?!
We cottoned on to your plan, missy. We destroyed the devices you gave us.
You told us those access codes would disable all of Stark security!
They do! Don't they?
Lucky for you, Callee...